WWF

WILD FRIENDS

DOLPHIN SPLASHDOWN

By Linda Chapman and Michelle Misra

Illustrated by Damien Jones

RED FOX

WWF WILD FRIENDS: DOLPHIN SPLASHDOWN

A RED FOX BOOK 978 1 782 95167 4

First published in Great Britain by Red Fox,
an imprint of Random House Children's Publishers UK
A Random House Group Company

This edition published 2013

1 3 5 7 9 10 8 6 4 2

Random House Children's Publishers UK uses the WWF marks
under license from WWF-World Wide Fund for Nature.
WWF is not the manufacturer of this product.

WWF-UK is a charity reg'd in England and Wales (no. 1081247) and
in Scotland (no. SC039593) and relies on support from its members and the public. This
product is produced under license from WWF-UK (World Wide Fund for Nature) Trading
Limited, Godalming, Surrey, GU7 1XR.
Thank you for your help.

The Random House Group Limited supports the Forest Stewardship Council (FSC®),
the leading international forest certification organization. Our books carrying the FSC
label are printed on FSC®-certified paper. FSC is the only forest certification scheme
endorsed by the leading environmental organizations, including Greenpeace. Our paper
procurement policy can be found at www.randomhouse.co.uk/environment.

MIX
Paper from
responsible sources
FSC
www.fsc.org   FSC® C016897

Set in Bembo MT
Red Fox Books are published by Random House Children's Publishers UK,
61–63 Uxbridge Road, London W5 5SA

www.**randomhousechildrens**.co.uk
www.**randomhouse**.co.uk

Addresses for companies within The Random House Group Limited
can be found at: www.randomhouse.co.uk/offices.htm

THE RANDOM HOUSE GROUP Limited Reg. No. 954009

A CIP catalogue record for this book is available from the British Library.

Printed and bound in Great Britain by Clays Ltd, St Ives plc

Danny started the engine and they headed back towards the beach. But as he started to turn the boat round, Emily spotted something. 'Look!' she gasped. She was sure she had just seen a grey fin cutting through the water.

'What? I can't see anything,' her dad said.

'There was a dolphin, I'm sure!'

Mr Oliver stood up and scanned the sea. 'I think you imagined it, sweetheart. I can't see any— WHOA!' he shouted as a shape exploded up out of the water, jumping in a high arc. Its wet grey sides shone in the sunlight and its dark eyes seemed to wink as it plunged back into the water sending water splashing all over them.

"It is a dolphin!" cried Emily in delight. 'And not just one!' She suddenly saw other fins in the water. 'It's lots of them!'

Meet all of Emily's
WILD FRIENDS

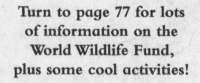

Turn to page 77 for lots
of information on the
World Wildlife Fund,
plus some cool activities!

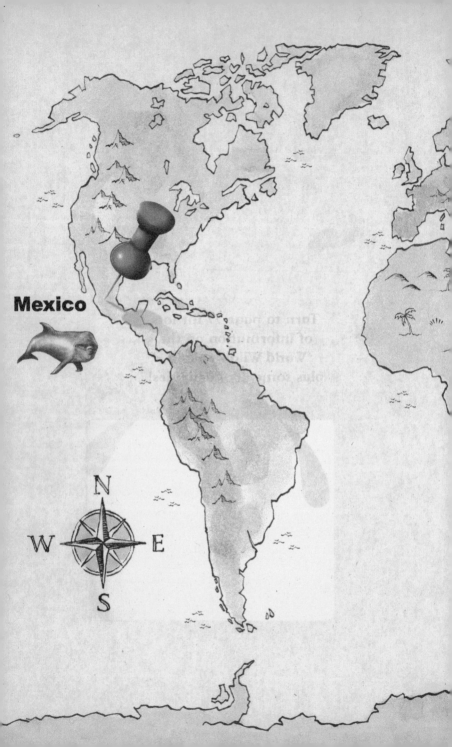

Mexico

A Dolphin Display

"Where shall we go next?" Emily Oliver called to her mum and dad. She was standing in front of a large map that showed the whole of the Florida Marine Park and Aquarium. The sun was beating down, making her glad she was just wearing shorts and a T-shirt.

Her parents joined her, and Emily traced with her finger the route they had taken since arriving that morning: they had started by walking through the viewing rooms of the coral reef gallery, where they had seen shoals of little fish swooping through the brightly coloured coral.

After that they had come outside for the water walk, where they had seen cute otters gambolling in streams and pink flamingos wading delicately through a lake.

"We could go to the water adventure zone," suggested Emily's dad, pointing to an area that showed a picture of water cannons and a large pirate ship.

But Emily didn't want to play in the water. "No, I'd like to see more animals," she said.

"That suits me!" her mum said with a smile, and Mr Oliver nodded too. They loved animals as much as Emily did! They both worked for an organization called WWF. It was a charity that worked hard to protect endangered animals and their

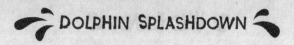

habitats around the world. The Olivers travelled a lot with their jobs – and in the school holidays Emily often went with them. This was the first holiday in ages where they had just come away to relax, rather than being on WWF business. So far, they had spent two days in Disney World and chilled out in the beautiful house they were renting. But Emily had started to miss seeing animals, so they had decided to visit the nearby marine park.

"How about we walk along the wetlands trail and see some alligators?" suggested Mrs Oliver.

Emily rubbed her nose. "Maybe . . ." She loved all animals, but alligators weren't her favourite.

"Or how about this?" said her dad, checking out a whiteboard next to the map. "It says that there's a dolphin show in the dolphin and sea lion centre in fifteen minutes. If we go quickly, we'll just get there in time."

Dolphins! Emily nodded hard. She loved dolphins! "Oh, please can we do that?"

"Dolphins it is, then!" her mum declared. "Come on. We'd better hurry!"

The dolphin pool was made out of white concrete. It was large and oval, with three metal stepladders and little platforms at the top of each one. The water was very blue. People could sit and watch the show on the tiered seating around the pool. By the time the Olivers arrived, the show was about to start and there were just a few spaces left

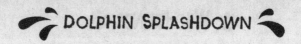

right at the back. They climbed up the steps and sat down.

"Do you know much about dolphins?" Emily's dad asked.

Emily had never seen a dolphin in real life, but she knew a bit about them. "They're mammals like whales, not fish like sharks," she said, remembering what had been said on the documentary she'd seen on TV. "That means they can't breathe underwater – they have to come up for air every so often. They breathe through their blowholes, not their mouths, and they give birth to their babies and feed them on milk." Her dad nodded. "Oh, and they're very intelligent."

"That's right," Mr Oliver said. "They've got the largest brain of any marine mammal. They live in groups called pods, and can talk to each other using sounds like squeaks and whistles, and also by slapping their tails on the water."

"Don't they sometimes work as a team to catch fish?" Emily said, remembering one of the things she had read.

Her dad nodded. "They've also been known to team up in order to rescue other dolphins in trouble or even to help humans in danger. A group of lifeguards were once stranded in deep water and a shark was approaching. Forty dolphins surrounded them and kept the shark away until help came."

"Wow!" Emily breathed. Dolphins really were incredible.

Just then music started to play and a voice crackled out over the loudspeaker. "*Welcome, everyone! Welcome to our dazzling dolphin display! Prepare to meet our two dolphins – give a big hand for Flicker and Splash!*"

Emily quickly pulled her camera out of her bag as three dolphin trainers came out.

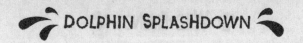

Two were wearing shorts and one was in a
wetsuit. An underwater door opened, and
two grey dolphins came streaking into the
pool. They burst out of the water together,
sending droplets spraying everywhere as
they arced over and dived back under in
perfect time. As everyone clapped
and cheered, they popped up again,
their mouths open, as if they
were grinning. They
had pale grey
skin and
sparkling
dark
eyes.

They were absolutely beautiful. Emily tried to take some photos, but the dolphins were too far away. She wished she was closer, not sitting right at the back.

One of the trainers stepped forward. She had a radio microphone on. "Hi, everyone. I'm Tamsin and I'm the head dolphin trainer here. Flicker and Splash will be showing you some of the things they can do. Flicker, say hi!"

The larger dolphin did a backward flip into the water. The crowd whooped and cheered. Tamsin threw him a silver fish from a bucket.

"And now, Splash, it's your turn to say hi!"

The second dolphin waved a flipper.

"Time to get this show started!" Tamsin cried.

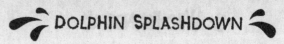

There was
another burst of
music, and then
the dolphins
started performing
the tricks they had
been trained to do.
They leaped up to
the height of the tallest
platform to get a fish,
jumped through hoops,
twisted and turned, and
carried a flag through the water.
The trainer in the wetsuit got into the pool
and they let her hold their fins and swam
around the pool with her. After each trick
they got a fish. The crowd clapped and
cheered, but as the show went on, Emily
started to feel a little bit torn. The dolphins
did appear to be enjoying themselves, but
she couldn't help thinking that they would

be happier out in the sea, in their natural habitat, rather than living in a concrete pool and performing for people every day. It reminded her of visiting a zoo and watching an orang-utan playing with toys, or a bored-looking lion lying in his carefully constructed enclosure. However healthy and well cared for the animal was in captivity, she still always felt sad that they were no longer out in the wild.

She sat back in her seat, and when the show finished, she clapped but she didn't cheer. Her mum gave her a questioning look. "Are you all right?"

"Yep," Emily said quietly. They were surrounded by people saying how amazing the show had been; she didn't want to start

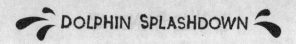

claiming that it wasn't fair on the dolphins. But as they climbed down from their seats and left the dolphin viewing area, her mum nudged her.

"Something's up. What is it, Em?"

"It's the dolphins," Emily admitted. "I wish they were out in the wild still – not stuck here, performing for people all the time."

Her mum gave her an understanding look. "I know. I feel like that too. But I did check out this park before we came, and they keep their dolphins in very good conditions. They only have dolphins that have been bred in captivity or been orphaned as babies – dolphins who've never really known any other life and who would struggle to survive in the wild."

Emily felt a bit better. "I'd love to see dolphins in the wild," she said.

"Maybe you will one day," her dad said.

"It's certainly an amazing sight."

Just then, Mrs Oliver's mobile phone rang. She checked the number. "Oh, I'd better take this call. It's from work." She walked a little distance away.

"How about we get an ice cream while we wait?" Mr Oliver said to Emily.

"OK!"

Emily and her dad spent ages choosing their flavours. In the end Mr Oliver went for three different types of chocolate – milk, plain and white. Emily decided on a scoop of mango, a scoop of strawberry and a scoop of toffee flavour, with loads of cookie sprinkles on top! They sat down on a wall and ate their ice

creams as they waited for Mrs Oliver to get off the phone. Emily was just crunching up the end of her cone when her mum came over. She had a strange look on her face.

"Anything important?" Mr Oliver asked.

"Um . . . yes." She looked at Emily. "You know you just said you'd really like to see dolphins in the wild . . ."

"Yes," Emily said, hope suddenly flaring up inside her.

Her mum smiled. "Well, provided you don't mind cutting our holiday short, I think your wish could come true!"

To Mexico!

Emily stared at her mum. "You mean, we can go somewhere and see wild dolphins?"

"If you and Dad don't mind leaving Florida . . . then yes," her mum said. "I've just been asked to go to Mexico to take photographs of a coral reef. It's not too far away . . . and there are lots of dolphins around there . . ." She looked questioningly at Mr Oliver.

He put an arm around her. "If you want to go, and Emily's happy with that, then it's fine by me."

"Oh yes, I'm *very* happy!" said Emily,

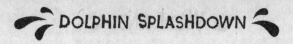

her eyes shining at the thought of seeing dolphins – and probably lots of other animals and birds too! "I like Florida, but I'd rather go and see more dolphins than stay here!"

Her mum smiled. "Then that's just what we'll do!"

The very next morning, the Olivers packed up and set off for the airport. They took a short flight to Cancún, and then picked up a jeep and drove for three hours down the coastal road. Every so often the trees would clear and they would catch glimpses of the turquoise Caribbean Sea lapping against a deserted beach of snow-white sand. It was absolutely beautiful.

"What other animals might we see?" Emily asked as she looked out of the window.

"Well, we might see manatees and turtles as well as dolphins," her mum said. "And on the coral reef there'll be all sorts of different fish, as well as seahorses and octopus, starfish and eels."

"And on land you'll see lots of birds," her dad added. "Wild flamingos as well as brown pelicans, spoonbills and herons. Look!" He pointed. "There's a parrot now!"

Emily watched in delight as a parrot swooped across the road in front of them. It had bright green feathers and red patches on its cheeks.

"We might see howler and spider monkeys in the trees," said her mum. "And lots of butterflies and dragonflies. There's so much wildlife around here."

Emily sighed happily. It was brilliant to be on an animal adventure again!

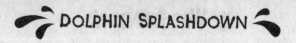

The road grew bumpier. They passed
a fishing village, with small wooden huts
and motorboats and nets pulled up onto
the beach alongside piles of driftwood;
people were mending nets and hanging
out washing. A little while later, Mr Oliver
turned onto a sandy track, carefully
avoiding the huge potholes. They bumped
closer and closer to the sea, until finally
they arrived at a wooden lodge where
WWF had set up a temporary base. Its big

veranda overlooked the deserted sandy bay, and it was surrounded by palm trees – some with striped hammocks strung between them. Two boats were pulled up onto the beach, well away from the water. As Emily got out of the jeep, the warmth of the late afternoon sun hit her and she was glad of the sea breeze that blew through her dark hair.

A woman came down the steps of the lodge. She had short black hair and friendly brown eyes. She was wearing light shorts and a T-shirt with a picture of a shoal of flying fish. "Hi." She gave them a warm smile. "Are you the Olivers?"

"That's right," Emily's mum said, shaking hands with her. "I'm Heather, and this is my husband, Mike, and my daughter, Emily."

"I'm Jess," the woman said. "I'm one of the marine biologists. It's lovely to have you here. Please – come in."

They followed her up the steps. Inside was a large, airy common room, painted white, with big sliding glass doors that led out onto the veranda. A large older lady in a brightly patterned dress, her dark hair piled up in a bun, came out to meet them.

"This is Rosa, our cook," said Jess.

"*Hola*," Rosa said with a friendly smile.

Emily knew that meant hello in Spanish – the language spoken in Mexico. "*Hola*," she replied. On the plane her dad had taught her some Spanish phrases. "*Cómo estás?*" she asked, slightly falteringly. It meant "How are you?"

Rosa ruffled her hair. "*Muy bien, chiquita*,"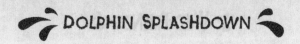

she said, looking delighted. "You speak Spanish?"

"Only a little," said Emily.

Rosa chuckled. "Soon you learn more! Now, I go get drinks." And she bustled off.

Jess helped the Olivers bring their luggage in from the car and showed them to their bedrooms on the first floor. Each one had a ceiling fan whirring round, long white net curtains and views out over the ocean. Emily unpacked, gave her hands a quick wash in the sink, ran a brush through her hair and then hurried back downstairs. Everyone else had moved out onto the veranda, where Rosa had set out a tray of drinks. Mr and Mrs Oliver had a cold beer each, while Emily had been left a delicious pink drink.

"*Agua fresca*," Jess told her when she asked what it was called. "It's made of papaya fruit, sugar and water."

"It's really nice!" said Emily. "I wish we had this at home!"

Rosa had also left them a plate of deep-fried tortilla triangles. Jess explained that they were called *totopos*.

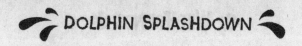

"These are just to keep you going. Rosa will be out with some more food very soon," she said. "You must be hungry after your journey."

Emily's stomach rumbled in agreement. It seemed a long time since their sandwich lunch. She wondered what the food would be like here in Mexico. Her dad had told her it was often hot and spicy.

She needn't have worried, though. The food Rosa brought out was delicious! There was a big platter of tortillas filled with pieces of chicken or beef. They were served with shredded lettuce and sour cream. There was also a bowl of tomato salsa. When Emily bit into her first chicken tortilla, she couldn't help giving a sigh of pleasure. It was scrumptious.

Her dad spooned some salsa onto his, but when Emily tried it she needed to have a drink straight away. It was flavoured with chilli peppers and was very spicy!

For pudding there was a platter of fruit: pineapple, melon, papaya, watermelon – and something Emily hadn't tried before called custard fruit, which looked a bit like a large, very knobbly, dark green pear. It had a sweet white flesh inside and tasted like a mixture of banana,

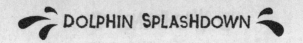

pineapple and strawberry.

"This is wonderful!" she said.

As they all tucked in, Jess told them more about the projects WWF was running in the area.

"We're trying to monitor the coral reef along the coast here," she explained. "It's the Mesoamerican Reef – the second largest in the world. It's hugely important because of the number of different species that live there. Over-fishing and tourists not taking proper care when they visit are causing a lot of damage, so some species are dying out. In the nature reserve, which is a bit further along the coast, good fishing practices are being enforced, and the tourism is carefully monitored, but outside the reserve it's a different story. We need to take photographs so we can compare it to how it was a few years ago and provide a record of how it has changed."

"My camera's ready and waiting!" Emily's mother declared. "Just take me there and show me what you want me to photograph." She had taken photographs for WWF all around the world, from the cold of the Arctic to the jungles of Borneo.

"We'll go tomorrow," said Jess. "We'll start by taking some photos up near Playa del Carmen and then work our way back down here." She looked at Mr Oliver and Emily. "You're very welcome to come with us – or we could drop you off in Playa to do some shopping."

Emily glanced at her dad. She didn't want to go and look round a town – she wanted to see some animals!

Luckily her dad understood her look. "I rather think Emily was hoping to see some wild dolphins rather than shops.

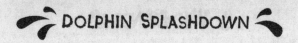
Weren't you, Em?"

"Oh yes!" she said.

"No problem." Jess smiled. "You can see them here. We're also running a dolphin project from the base. Danny is the marine biologist in charge of that – you'll meet him later. I'm sure he'll take you out to look for dolphins tomorrow if that's what you want. Right now he's out meeting the fishermen in one of the villages, but we can ask him when he gets back. We're trying to monitor the wild dolphin population and train the local fishermen to use safer fishing techniques that will protect the dolphins as well as the endangered turtles that live in these waters. Far too many of them are dying because they get caught in fishing nets."

The conversation moved on to some of the other projects the Olivers had been involved in around the world. Emily yawned and sank back in her chair, letting their voices wash over her. The sun was setting, casting a soft golden light across the sky. She stared out towards the horizon. Somewhere out there, wild dolphins were swimming. She wrapped her arms around herself, and thought, *Oh, please let me see some tomorrow!*

Out on the Sea

When Emily woke up the next morning,
it took her a few seconds to remember
where she was. But as she sat up in bed, it
all came flooding back. She was in Mexico,
of course! She jumped up and pulled open
the curtains. Bright light came flooding
in. Through the window she could see the
glittering sea and the few wispy white
clouds that drifted across the sky. Emily felt
happiness rush through her.

Pulling on her shorts and a T-shirt, she
crept into her mum and dad's room. They
were still asleep, so she made her way
downstairs, and into the common room.

Rosa had set out some fresh fruit, tortillas, little bread rolls and thin slices of a spicy red sausage on the breakfast table. A man in his thirties was sitting on the veranda eating a plate of tortillas, sausage and eggs with red spicy sauce on top. He was tanned, with blond hair and a stubbly beard.

"Hi there," he said, turning round as he heard her come in. "I guess you must be Emily. I'm Danny. I hear you're a bit of a dolphin fan like me."

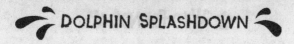

"Oh, yes!" said Emily. "I love them!" She liked Danny immediately. He had friendly brown eyes and a wide smile. "Jess said we might be able to go out in a boat with you today."

"You sure can. Now, why don't you help yourself to some breakfast?" he said, waving to the table. "There's hot chocolate or coffee in the two silver pots, and Rosa will cook you some eggs too if you want."

"No, thank you. This all looks great," said Emily, helping herself to some fruit and rolls. Then she poured herself a cup of steaming hot chocolate. She breathed in as she poured it. It smelled delicious! She carried her plate and cup outside and sat down next to Danny.

"So, what do you know about dolphins?" he asked her.

She told him everything she had learned.

"Not bad," he said, looking impressed.

"Did you also know that the Spanish word for dolphin is *delfín*, and that they use echolocation to hunt their prey?"

Emily shook her head and sipped the hot, slightly spicy chocolate. "What's that?"

"It's when an animal like a dolphin sends out a series of sounds – dolphins make a series of clicks. They listen to the echoes that come back through the water and use those echoes to help them work out how far away objects are and what shape they are."

Emily was fascinated. "Don't bats do something like that too?"

"That's right," said Danny. "But I prefer dolphins."

"Me too," agreed Emily. They smiled at each other.

"Hey, do you want to watch some videos I've taken out in the sea here?" Danny asked suddenly.

"Yes, please!" said Emily.

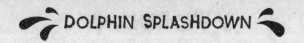

Danny got out his iPad, and soon they were both watching videos of dolphins jumping and playing. Emily loved the way they opened their mouths as if they were smiling. It was wonderful to see them  swimming in the open sea rather than performing in a marine park. She really hoped she would get to see some for real!

Just then Mr and Mrs Oliver came downstairs. "Look at this!" Emily called, beckoning them over, and they watched the videos too.

Mrs Oliver smiled. "I almost wish I was coming out with you today. I love dolphins. Maybe I can come out for a quick boat trip before we leave . . ."

"You're on," said Danny with a grin.

After breakfast they all got ready to go out. Jess and Mrs Oliver loaded up the car with cameras, wetsuits and scuba-diving gear and set off back up the coast. Then Emily put on her swimsuit and lots of waterproof sunscreen. She pulled her shorts and T-shirt on over the top, tied her dark hair back in a ponytail and put on her baseball cap and trainers. She was ready to go!

Her dad and Danny brought out a large cool box full of drinks and snacks in case they got hungry while they were out, then pulled the boat, *The Trident*, down to the

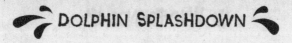

water, and they all got in. Danny started
the engine, and they chugged out towards
the open sea, the wind blowing in their
faces, keeping them cool despite the heat
of the sun. They travelled over the reef
and then further out, where Danny said
the dolphins were most likely to be. Emily
scanned the ocean. Where were they?

They motored up and down, but there
was no sign of any dolphins. After a
while a fishing boat chugged past them,
heading towards the nearby village with
a haul of fish and lobster. They saw three
men aboard it, all dressed in white vests

and shorts and baseball
caps; their nets were
piled in a heap on
the deck. The oldest
one, his face tanned
and wrinkled from
many years in the
sun, raised his hand and
called out a greeting.

"*Buenos días!*"

Danny waved back. "*Buenos días*, Vincent!
Have you had a good catch today?"

"So so," the fisherman said. "Maybe
more tomorrow – yes, yes, I know," he said
before Danny could say anything more. He
winked. "Maybe I change my nets and my
luck it will change. *Adiós, mi amigo.*" And he
turned his boat for home.

"That's Vincent, one of the local
fishermen," Danny explained to Mr Oliver
and Emily. "He's one of the most senior

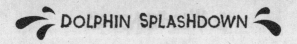

fishermen in the village and I've been trying to talk to him about changing the way he fishes. I think if only he agreed, then the others would too."

"How's it all going?" Mr Oliver asked.

Danny scratched his head. "There's still a lot of work to do. Vincent and the others are always very friendly – they are kind people – but their methods of fishing have worked for them for years and it's hard to make them see the benefits of changing their ways. It can be done though: there's a village on the reserve where they are using nets with turtle exclusion devices to keep turtles and dolphins from getting caught up in the nets. I wish we could persuade the fishermen around here to change too."

"So do I, if it stops dolphins and turtles getting caught in the nets," said Emily, shuddering at the thought of creatures trapped and in pain.

They motored on, still searching for dolphins. Emily began to wonder if they would see any that day after all. Danny stopped the engine and they bobbed around on the water as they shared out the lunch.

"I guess it looks like the dolphins are swimming somewhere else today," he said as they packed away the leftovers. "We can always try again tomorrow."

"Can't we stay a little longer?" Emily begged.

But her dad shook his head. "Danny's got other work to do, Em. We can't take up all his time."

Danny started the engine, but as he turned the boat round, Emily spotted something. "Look!" she gasped. She was sure she had just seen a grey fin cutting through the water.

"What? I can't see anything," her dad said.

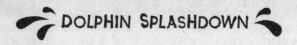

"There was a dolphin – I'm sure there was!"

Mr Oliver stood up and scanned the sea. "I think you imagined it, sweetheart. I can't see any— WHOA!" he shouted as a shape exploded up out of the water, jumping in a high arc. Its wet grey sides shone in the sunlight and its dark eyes seemed to wink as it plunged back into the sea, sending water splashing all over them.

"It *is* a dolphin!" cried Emily in delight. "And not just one!" She suddenly saw other fins in the water. "There's lots of them!"

Dolphins Everywhere!

"Look!" Emily gasped as three more silver dolphins arced into the air. There were at least twenty of them around the boat now. Danny turned off the engine and they bobbed about on the water, watching the creatures in delight. The dolphins seemed to know they had an audience. They dived and leaped across the waves. Most stayed away from the boat, but one came right up beside it and poked its head out of the water. It looked at Emily.

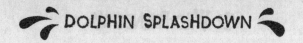

It was much smaller than the others – just a baby still. It whistled inquisitively.

Emily smiled and copied the sound. Then she added a couple of clicks. The young dolphin clicked its tongue back, and then, with a splash of its tail, dived under the surface. Emily tried to see where it had gone, and suddenly there it was again! It had surfaced on the other side of the boat, within touching distance. It looked eagerly at Emily, its dark eyes sparkling.

She longed to stroke its smooth grey head. "Can I touch it?" she asked Danny.

"It's better not to," he replied. "I'm sorry," he added, seeing her disappointment. "But sea creatures should really be left alone – even friendly ones like these dolphins. It's safer for them if they don't become too used to humans. I know it's tempting, but it really is better if you just watch – unless you have to touch them because they are in trouble."

Emily nodded. She understood. Wild
animals like these dolphins had to stay
wild to remain safe. Although no one on
the trip today would ever do anything to
harm a dolphin, maybe the next human
who came along would be different:
teaching the baby dolphin to come and be
stroked could put its life in danger. *No*, she
thought. *I'd rather just watch than risk that.*

The little dolphin ducked its head
into the sea and then popped up again,
shooting water out of its blowhole. It
gave Emily a cheeky look, and swam in
a circle before clicking its tongue at her
as if saying hello. She clicked back. It was
like she was introducing herself in dolphin
language. The dolphin swam around in
rapid circles before popping up beside the
boat again. She waved and, to her delight,
it copied her, raising one of its flippers.

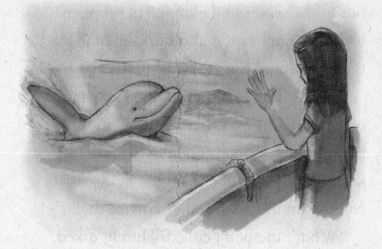

Emily giggled, and the dolphin blew water out of its blowhole, almost as if it was laughing too.

"It seems to have taken a shine to you!" said Danny.

"How old do you think it is?" Emily asked.

"It's a she, and she's almost exactly six months old," said Danny. "This is a pod I know well. Do you see that dark mark on her flipper?"

As if the dolphin understood, she reared

out of the water and clapped her flippers
together. Emily spotted a dark smudge on
the right-hand one. "Yes."

"That's how I recognize her. Her mum
is that dolphin over there," said Danny,
pointing out a nearby adult who was
keeping a watchful eye on the baby. "I
call the mum Cowrie after cowrie shells."

"What's the baby called?" Emily asked.

"I haven't thought of a name yet. You
can think of one, if you like," Danny
offered.

"Really?" Emily breathed.

He nodded.

Emily watched the baby swim around
in a circle. What could she call her? Names
ran through her head: Star? Silky? Silver?
None of them seemed quite right.

"I bet Mum would love to be here
photographing these beauties instead of
taking pictures of coral," said Mr Oliver.

Coral. Emily frowned thoughtfully. Yes! "Can we call the baby Coral?"

"That's a great name," agreed Danny. "Coral she is!"

Emily leaned over the side of the boat and whistled to the little dolphin. Coral whistled back, and then jumped into the air

and splashed down into the water again. Soon the pod started to lose interest in the boat and swam away. Emily watched them leaping and diving in twos and threes.

Cowrie came over and nudged her baby. Coral took one last look at Emily and then followed her mother back to join the others.

"Bye," Emily called after her.

Her dad put his arm around her shoulders. "Happy now?"

"Oh yes," she said. It had been wonderful. She'd seen more dolphins than she had ever imagined. The memories would stay with her for ever.

"Can we come back out on the sea tomorrow?" she asked eagerly.

"Sure," said Danny, starting the motor up again.

Emily sat at the back of the boat looking out to sea as they headed towards the shore. Somewhere deep in the waters out there, Coral was diving and swimming with her mum and the rest of her pod.

Coral Reef Adventure

They arrived back at the lodge in the middle of the afternoon. Mrs Oliver hadn't returned yet, so Emily explored the beach and played in the shallows while her dad read.

The sea was beautifully warm. She sat on the sand and let the gentle waves lap around her toes. Tiny silver fish were swimming in the clear water. She tried to see if they would swim into her hands, but they always darted away. She looked further out towards the darker blue water where the reef was. It would be amazing to go and snorkel there. She hoped she'd be allowed.

After a while her dad joined her, and they played beach cricket together until Danny, Jess and Emily's mum returned.

"Come and see the photos!" Mrs Oliver said when Emily ran to meet her. "The reef's incredible!"

They went inside, and she downloaded the photos onto her laptop, then showed them to Emily. There were corals of all shapes and sizes – tall blue pillars, pink coral with branches like trees, and large mounds of yellow and purple

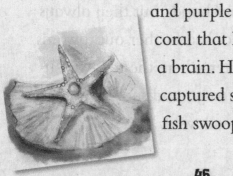

coral that looked a bit like a brain. Her mum had captured shoals of orange fish swooping through the

water, orange starfish and
feathery seaweed. There
were red crabs scuttling
along the bottom and an
eel whisking out of a cave.
It all looked beautiful, but
as Emily studied the scene
more closely, she could see
damaged areas – corals that
had been broken, and gaps
in the reef where coral shards
littered the sand.

"This is the problem," her
mum said, pointing out some
of the damage. "It may not
look like much, but when
you compare these photos to how the reef
looked five years ago, you can see how
quickly it is going downhill." She shook her
head. "This reef has taken millions of years
to form, and it's being destroyed so quickly."

"I wish I could see it for real," Emily said longingly.

"Well, how about coming out with us tomorrow?" her mum said. "In the morning, Jess and I are heading for the bit of reef beside this nearby fishing village. You could come with us and snorkel."

"Now that sounds a very good idea!" Mr Oliver said, coming up behind them. "You can count me in too."

"Great." Mrs Oliver smiled. "So how was your trip out to see the dolphins?"

"Brilliant!" said Emily. She told her mum all about it while they went to get changed for supper.

Rosa served them another magnificent meal on the veranda, starting with chicken soup with a dash of lime, followed by fresh prawns cooked with coconut and pepper, and pork rubbed with a red spice and baked in a banana leaf. Afterwards they

ate *churros* – sugar-coated doughnut strips –
and drank mugs of hot chocolate. Emily felt
wonderfully happy, but she was so tired that
she soon fell asleep in her chair, and her dad
had to carry her up to bed.

"Night-night, sweetheart," he said as he
tucked her up. "Have you had a good day?"

"Oh, yes!" Emily murmured sleepily.
"What time are we going to the reef
tomorrow?"

"As soon as we all get up. The earlier the
better." He kissed her head. "So you'd better
get some sleep while you can."

Emily shut her eyes and snuggled down. Listening to the ceiling fan whirring overhead, she thought about the next day. Would she see eels and manta rays? Sea horses and starfish? More dolphins? Lost in happy thoughts, she was soon asleep again.

The next morning, everyone was eager to get started. After a quick breakfast they loaded up one of the boats with scuba-diving gear, snorkelling masks and flippers, Mrs Oliver's cameras and another big cool box full of drinks and snacks. They all climbed in and set off for the reef.

Emily sat at the back of the boat, watching trails of white foam spreading out behind them.

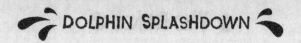

As they approached the reef, Mr Oliver nudged Emily. "Look, I think there are some dolphins over there!" He nodded out towards the horizon.

Emily shielded her eyes from the sun. Yes – her dad was right! She could make out grey fins cutting through the water, and as she watched, two dolphins leaped up and skimmed across the surface before diving back in. The pod was heading away from the reef. "Can we go after them?" She hoped it was the same dolphin pod they'd met yesterday – perhaps she'd see Coral.

"Not now, Em," her mum said. "I need to take photographs here on the reef."

Emily was disappointed. She'd have loved to say hello to the dolphins again, but she knew her mum's work had to come first.

"I'll take you out in the boat tomorrow again," Danny offered.

She smiled back at him. "Thanks."

He turned off the engine and threw out the anchor, and Jess turned to the Olivers. "Now it's time for us all to do some diving and snorkelling!" she said.

The boat bobbed slightly on the calm sea as they got their equipment ready. Jess and Emily's mum were already wearing wetsuits, and Emily's dad helped them on with their scuba-diving tanks so that they could breathe under the water as they explored the deeper parts of the reef. They put the breathing tubes into their mouths, sat on the edge of the boat, waved goodbye and then flipped backwards into the water with a big splash. The boat rocked for a few

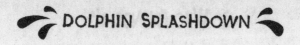

seconds and then steadied itself.

"I wish I could scuba-dive," said Emily, imagining what it must be like to go right deep down into the ocean.

"You can learn when you're a bit older," her dad promised. "You'll see a lot just snorkelling. Remember to wet the inside of your mask."

Emily nodded. She knew that this was important – it stopped the inside getting steamed up. She put her flippers on and then her mask. Her dad did the same. Danny was going to stay with the boat.

"Here goes!" said Mr Oliver. He put the snorkel tube into his mouth and climbed over the side of the boat, using the ladder. Emily quickly

followed him. She gasped as the cold hit her
– the sun's rays hadn't warmed the water
yet. But as soon as she started swimming,
she forgot all about the cold. There was so
much to see!

The reef was a multicoloured world
of coral, rocks and seaweed. Everywhere

she looked there was a different bright
colour. A shoal of blue and yellow fish
came swooping past her, followed by some
bright orange, black and white clown fish.

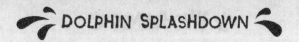

And then, suddenly, she spotted a turtle
swimming straight towards her! She trod
water as it swerved past and then dived
deeper, its flippers powering it down towards
the sea bed. Emily felt a thrill run through
her. She wished she could follow it!

She started swimming again, her eyes

taking in everything. Her dad was up
ahead, looking at a red starfish. She gave
him a thumbs up and carried on, swimming
round a tall column of blue coral.

Emily came to a stop as a movement
in the water ahead suddenly caught her
attention. Something was twisting and
turning this way and that, churning up sand
and debris. What was it? It was obviously
some sort of sea creature. Through the cloud
of sand she caught sight of a grey fin with
fishing net wrapped around it, and then she
heard a rattle of frightened clicks. Oh no! A
little dolphin had got caught up in a fishing
net!

Emily swam closer and saw a dark
smudge on its flipper. It was Coral, the baby
dolphin she'd met the day before! Coral's
eyes were full of panic. She plunged first
one way and then the other, but the net was
tangled tightly around her fin and tail and
caught up in the sharp coral.

Emily's heart pounded. Dolphins couldn't
survive underwater for long – they needed
to come to the surface to breathe. What

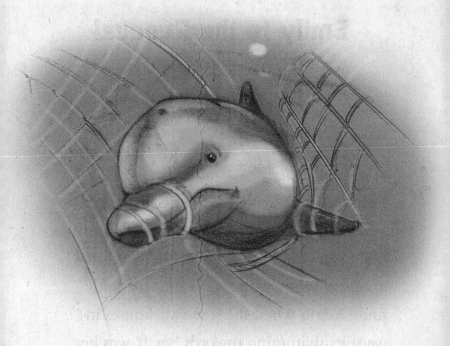

if Coral drowned? She had to try and
untangle her. But as the dolphin flipped
from one side to another, desperately trying
to free herself from the strong net, Emily
realized it was too dangerous. She couldn't
rescue Coral on her own.

She had to get help – and fast!

Emily to the Rescue!

Emily looked around for her dad. Where was he? She had no idea how long Coral had been caught in the net. She was just about to swim to the surface to try and find Danny when she saw two figures in wetsuits swimming towards her. It was her mum and Jess!

Emily couldn't shout because of her snorkel, so she waved at them frantically.

Puzzled, they swam over to her.

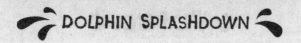

Emily didn't want to waste time explaining
– she would have to swim up to the surface
and take her mask off – so instead she
tugged her mum's arm and gestured round
the rock.

To her relief, her mum realized straight
away that something was badly wrong.
She and Jess followed Emily to where the
dolphin was trapped. Coral was still caught
up in the net, but her movements were
slowing down, as if she was running out of
energy. She flapped her tail feebly and then
rolled from side to side. She was obviously
very distressed.

Even through the masks, Emily could see
the shock on her mum and Jess's faces. They
swam over, but they weren't sure what to do,
and Emily could feel the precious seconds
slipping away. Maybe she could help by
fetching Danny? She quickly swam up to
the surface and saw her dad leaning over

the side of the boat, chatting to Danny. Her heart sank. They were a long way away. Starting to panic, Emily looked around and saw the fishing boat from the day before. Vincent was standing on deck with a couple of other fishermen. It was their net that Coral was trapped in! "Hola!" she shouted. "Hola!" She wished she knew the Spanish for help, but she didn't, so she just waved frantically as she trod water. "Over here! Please!" she cried, hoping he would understand.

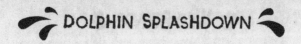

Vincent frowned and shaded his eyes from the sun. "What is it, *chica*?" he called. "Are you in trouble?"

Out of the corner of her eye Emily could see her dad and Danny had heard her shout too. Dad was climbing back into the boat and Danny was starting the engine, but Emily couldn't wait for them to arrive.

"I need your help!" she shouted to Vincent. She remembered the word for dolphin. "*El delfín!* It's caught in your net and needs to be set free."

Vincent's weather-beaten face instantly creased into a frown. He said something to the other fishermen in rapid Spanish as he ran over to the side of the boat and began to release the net.

Emily bobbed underneath the surface and motioned for her mum and Jess to move out of the way as one side of the net was released. It fell slowly through the water, allowing Coral to escape. At last she was free. But Emily could see at once that she was very weak. Mrs Oliver and Jess took her grey body in their arms and kicked up towards the surface. Emily followed behind.

"What's going on?" demanded Emily's dad. He and Danny had reached them now and stopped the motor boat.

"It's Coral!" gasped Emily. "She was caught in Vincent's net!" She stared at the little dolphin in her mum's arms. "Is she . . . is she dead?"

"No, she's still alive," said Mrs Oliver as

she and Jess trod water and held the dolphin up so she could breathe again.

Danny got into the water and checked Coral's heart. She gave a feeble flick of her tail and raised her head slightly.

"Is she going to be OK?" Emily's chest felt tight with worry.

"Yes, I think she's going to be fine," Danny said – to her relief. "She's had a bit of a scare, but she seems all right and her heartbeat is already returning to normal. Luckily she's young and strong."

Coral's eyes already looked a little brighter. "You can stroke her," Danny told Emily. "I know I said not to touch her yesterday, but this is a different situation. I think she'll enjoy being touched. It may help her recover from the shock."

Emily stroked Coral's smooth head. At first the little dolphin's

eyes were hazy, but then they seemed to focus on Emily.

"You're going to be all right," Emily whispered. She remembered their conversation the day before and made a soft whistling sound.

Coral opened her mouth and gave a squeak.

Emily copied her. Coral's eyes grew brighter and she squeaked again, this time adding a whistle.

Vincent was watching closely and talking to the other fishermen, gesturing at the dolphin and Emily.

"So, what happened?" Emily's dad asked.

Emily explained how she had found the dolphin and gone looking for help.

"She's been very lucky," Danny said. "Another few minutes and I think she

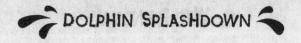

would have run out of air."

Mrs Oliver squeezed Emily's arm. "Well done, Em. It was good thinking to ask Vincent for help. If he hadn't released the net, we wouldn't have been able to free her."

Coral pushed Emily with her nose and Emily kissed her head. "I'm just glad we were snorkelling here."

"The question is what we do now," said Danny. "She'll find it very hard to manage on her own without her mother. She needs to be with her pod."

"I think we have to let her take her chances," said Jess, "and hope she finds her pod again."

"You're right," Danny agreed. "Let's see if she'll swim away."

Mrs Oliver and Jess gently released Coral in the water, and they all retreated a little to give her some space. For a moment

Coral didn't seem to know what to do.
She swam in small circles, making lots of
clicking sounds.

"Go on," said Mrs Oliver, pushing her
gently. "Find your pod."

Coral swam a little way off, still clicking.

"She's going!" said Mr Oliver hopefully.
But, on finding no other dolphins, Coral
seemed to lose heart. She flipped herself
round and headed back towards the
humans, preferring their company to the
empty sea. She swam over to Emily and
nudged her head against her.

Emily stroked her. "You can't stay with
us," she said as Coral whistled at her. "You
have to go."

But Coral didn't want to.

Jess looked anxiously at Danny. "What
are we going to do?"

"I don't know," he said. "Maybe we
should call a dolphin rescue centre. They

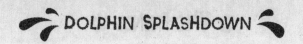

can take her in and try and release her into the wild when she's older."

"But if they can't, does that mean she'll live in captivity for the rest of her life?" asked Emily.

Danny nodded.

"No," she said quickly. She hated the thought of Coral becoming like the dolphins she'd seen in the marine park in Florida. She wanted her to live here in the sea where she belonged. She gave Coral a push, but Coral thought she was just playing, and bumped Emily's arm with her nose.

"Go on!" Emily told her.

The fishermen had been watching everything closely. "*El bebé delfín?*" called Vincent. "She will not go?"

Emily couldn't stop herself. She was so worried about Coral. "If you fished with other nets, things like this wouldn't happen!" she exclaimed. "Coral could have drowned, and now, even though she's free, she's lost her mother and the rest of her pod."

The fishermen turned and murmured to each other.

"You should listen to Danny! If you don't, other dolphins are going to die or be injured. Please!" Emily begged them. "Please stop using the nets! Coral would be dead now if we hadn't come along. As it is, she might end up living in captivity." Tears stung her eyes and she turned away, not wanting people to see her cry.

There was a moment's silence. Emily felt her mum gently squeeze her arm in support.

But suddenly there was a shout from the fishing boat. "*El delfin!*"

Emily looked up. Vincent was pointing

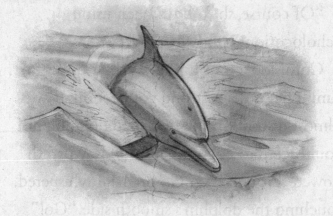

out to sea. She followed his gaze and saw
a dolphin coming towards them. She was
leaping over the waves, her grey body
arcing above the water as she dived and
jumped, dived and jumped. She surfaced
a little way from the boat and looked out
of the water anxiously. She whistled – and
Coral whistled back in delight.

"It's Cowrie, Coral's mother!" exclaimed
Danny.

"She must have been looking for Coral
and heard her clicks through the water,"
said Jess.

"Of course, she'd have been using echolocation!" said Mr Oliver.

Coral looked at Emily. As their gazes met, Emily felt a deep, strong connection. It was almost as though she and the baby dolphin could see into each other's minds. Warmth flowed through her. "Go on," she whispered, touching the dolphin's smooth side. "Go!"

With a joyful whistle, Coral dived under the water and swam towards her mother. Emily held onto the side of the boat and watched as Cowrie whooshed through the sea to meet her baby. They stopped and touched noses, their dark eyes shining with delight. Coral squeaked and clicked, as if

telling her mum all about her adventures. Emily felt a lump in her throat. The two dolphins looked so pleased to be reunited.

Emily felt her mum put an arm lightly around her shoulders. "A happy ending," Mrs Oliver said softly.

Emily nodded. It *was* for Coral, but what about all the other wild dolphins out there in the sea? Would they be so lucky? She turned to look at the fishermen. They were watching the dolphins with big smiles on their faces. Vincent was nodding slowly to himself. He caught sight of Emily's eyes on him.

"We change!" he announced to her. He pointed at Coral and Cowrie. "For them." Then he pointed at Emily.

"And for *la chica valiente*!" He shook his head. "Big nets? No! No more! That is what I say!" He turned to Danny. "Meet me this evening, *amigo*. We talk, and you tell us again how to fish to keep *los delfines* safe. I, Vincent, will make sure everyone is there and that everyone listens." He raised his hand to them. "*Adiós! Hasta luego!*"

"*Adiós!*" everyone called as he started his boat and chugged away.

Emily watched him go, feeling like she was going to burst with happiness.

"I can't believe it," said Danny, in astonishment. "I've been trying to persuade Vincent to change his ways for ages, and now a ten-year-old comes along and he agrees!"

Mr Oliver chuckled. "Emily has that effect on people. *La chica valiente*," he repeated. "That means 'the brave girl'."

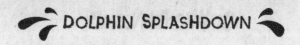

He smiled warmly at Emily. "I think he's right."

Emily blushed. "It wasn't just me – it was Coral and Cowrie who changed his mind too."

"Whatever changed his mind, I'm delighted," said Jess. "It'll make the seas a lot safer for the wild dolphins and turtles around here."

Mrs Oliver hugged Emily. "Well done, Em." She nodded out to sea. "And see Coral and Cowrie ... Don't they look happy?"

They all turned to where Coral and
Cowrie were whisking through the water,
playing a game of tag.

"They look *very* happy," Emily agreed
with a smile. She climbed into the boat, and
then she and her dad and Danny helped
Mrs Oliver and Jess take off their scuba
tanks and get in. The boat rocked gently in
the water.

Out at sea, Cowrie and Coral began to
head away to find their pod. As they
built up speed, they leaped out of
the water together,

side by side, their wet bodies sparkling in the sun. They skimmed over the surface and dived back in.

Emily leaned her head against her dad's shoulder.

"Are you happy now too?" he said to her.

"Oh yes," she whispered.

Coral was finally back where she belonged, safe with her mother, swimming wild and safe in the blue Caribbean Sea.

Read on for lots of amazing
dolphin facts, fun puzzles
and more about WWF

WWF

wwf.org.uk/gowild

Dolphin Fact File

Best feature: Bottlenose dolphins can swim at speeds of close to 35 kilometres per hour, although only for short bursts.

Size: Adult bottlenose dolphins are usually around 2.5 metres in length and 250kg in weight.

Favourite food: Their diet normally consists of crustaceans, squid and small fish.

Home: There are more than 30 species of dolphin. Most live in oceans across the world, but there are also 6 species of river dolphins, found in Brazil, China, Colombia, India, Nepal and Pakistan.

Current population: It is very difficult to estimate population numbers as there are many different species spanning a large geographic area.

Breeding and family: Female dolphins attain maturity between years 5 and 12, while male dolphins do so between ages 9 and 13. A calf is born after a gestation period of about 12 months. Usually, a single calf is born and the calves nurse for up to 18 months.

Life span: Their life expectancy is anything from 20 to 40 years.

Biggest threat: One of the greatest threats to dolphins is accidental entanglement in fishing gear – which can cause them to drown. Known as bycatch, this causes the deaths of more than 300,000 cetaceans (dolphins, porpoises and whales) every year. Water pollution is also a major threat.

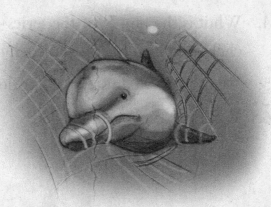

Bonus fact: Bottlenose dolphins can stay under water for up to 20 minutes.

Quiz time!

1. What were the names of either of the dolphins at the aquarium in Florida?

2. What does Jess have a picture of on her T-shirt?

3. What game do Danny, Mr Oliver and Emily play on the beach together?

4. What is the name for the series of clicks dolphins use to find each other?

5. What is the Spanish word for dolphin?

6. What is Coral's mum called?

*Answers: Flicker and Splash, flying fish,
cricket, echolocation, el delfin, Cowrie*

Word Search

Reading across, up, down and diagonally,
see if you can find all the listed words
in the grid below

A	Z	U	D	S	T	C	M	W	A	F	V	X
G	O	C	O	R	A	L	X	E	D	T	R	E
X	I	F	L	A	C	I	O	M	Z	Q	C	I
H	D	A	P	E	S	K	S	V	H	U	X	G
S	E	G	H	Z	P	T	R	I	D	E	N	T
I	C	N	I	U	I	A	J	N	E	R	A	J
F	L	A	N	X	O	O	L	C	A	T	P	A
R	E	D	M	E	N	B	G	E	V	O	M	D
A	H	I	O	E	A	X	D	N	I	H	Z	U
T	Z	O	U	A	R	C	B	T	U	A	O	L
S	T	F	X	C	W	A	O	X	F	E	E	R

CORAL	BOAT	TRIDENT	STARFISH
DOLPHIN	REEF	VINCENT	CAMERA

Word Scramble

The names of these characters from the book are all jumbled up. Can you unscramble them?

RLOAC

☐☐☐☐☐

NDNYA

☐☐☐☐☐

ORAS

☐☐☐☐

EICNVTN

☐☐☐☐☐☐☐

PASSHL

☐☐☐☐☐☐

Answers: Coral, Danny, Rosa, Vincent, Splash

Lost!

Poor Coral can't find her mum!
Can you lead her through the maze
to find her way back home?

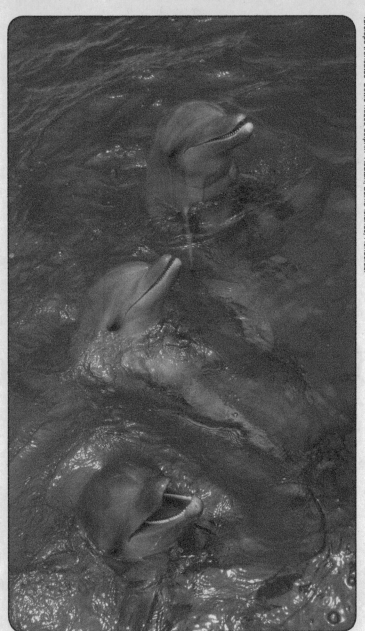

More about WWF

You're probably familiar with WWF's panda logo,
but did you know that WWF . . .

- Is the world's leading conservation organization.

- Was set up in 1961 (when TV was still black and white!).

- Works with lots of different people around the world, including governments, businesses and individuals, to make a difference to the world we live in.

- Is a charity and most of their money comes from members and supporters.

WWF's aim

The planet is our most precious resource and we need to take care of it! WWF want to build a future where people live in harmony with nature.

WWF are working towards this by:

- Protecting the natural world.

- Helping to limit climate change and find ways to help people deal with the impacts of it.

- Helping to change the way we live, so that the world's natural resources (like water and trees) are used more carefully, so they last for future generations.

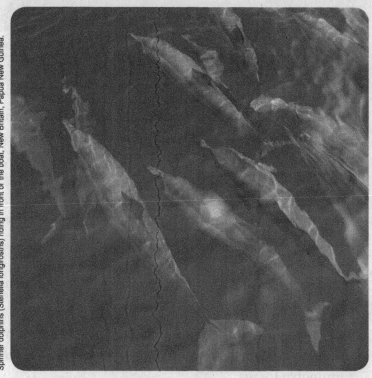

What do WWF do?

🐾 **Conservation** – Protect rare species of wild animals and plants as well as important ecosystems found in forests, rivers and seas.

🐾 **Climate change** – They don't just tackle the causes of global warming, but also the impacts of climate change on communities and environments.

🐾 **Sustainability** – Help to change the way we all live, particularly in richer developed countries like the UK, including decisions about what we eat, buy and use for fuel.

How can I help WWF?

There are lots of ways you can take action in your own home to help protect our beautiful planet and the people and animals that live on it. Here are a few ideas to get you started ...

Buy sustainable

One of the biggest threats to a lot of wildlife, including the giant panda, is loss of habitat. This is often from people cutting down trees to use in paper or wood products, or to make way for roads, and clearing areas to use for farming.

You can help stop this by only buying products that are sustainably farmed, or wood and paper products from sustainable forests.

So when you're out shopping with your mum or dad, look for:

- **Certified paper and wood products** (look for the FSC logo to tell if something is certified or not)

- **Products made from certified sustainable palm oil** (look for the RSPO logo to be sure that they are certified)

If your local shops don't stock these products – ask them why!

Reduce, reuse, recycle!

Households in the UK send 18 million tonnes of rubbish to landfill yearly. That's more than any other country in Europe!

Top five tips to reduce waste

Why don't you do some of these over a week and see how much less rubbish you throw away than normal?

Take a reuseable bag when you go to the shops, instead of picking up a new one.

Take any clothes, shoes, books or toys you don't want any more to a charity shop.

Clean out old food jars and pots to use for storage.

Get creative with your rubbish and make a kitchen-roll penguin.

Make postcards by cutting old birthday and Christmas cards in half, and give them to your friends.

"Go Wild!"

The way we live can affect people, wildlife and habitats all around the world. Making small but important changes to the way we act really can help to save polar bears in the Arctic or orang-utans in Borneo and Sumatra.

And this is what the Go Wild club is all about. It's your chance to learn more about some of the animals and habitats that we're working to protect. It's also about discovering what you can do in your own home to help look after the natural world.

By joining WWF's Go Wild club at *wwf.org.uk/gowildjoin*, you will recieve a member's pack and magazines that will take you on an incredible journey around the world, meeting some amazing animals and individuals. You'll find out what life's like for them and the threats they face to their environments.

As well as getting lots of Go Wild goodies, being a member means that you help WWF to continue their work. Join today and explore your wild side!

Don't miss Emily's adventure with adorable
panda cub Li, in the first Wild Friends story . . .

Read on for a sneak peek!

Exciting News!

Emily rested her pencil on the desk.
The other children at her table were still
copying the map of Great Britain from the
whiteboard at the front of the classroom.
Pushing her dark brown hair behind her
ears, Emily took a piece of scrap paper
and began to draw a panda. She sketched
a round body and head, coloured the little
ears in black and drew dark circles around
the eyes. She then added a stick of bamboo
in the panda's paws. She was concentrating
so hard she jumped when she heard her
teacher's voice behind her.

"Hmm," said Miss Haynes. "Pandas, Emily? I'm not sure *they're* found wild in the British Isles."

Emily blushed guiltily. "Sorry, Miss Haynes. It's just that I'm going to see them with my mum and dad in the summer holidays – in the mountains of China." Excitement bubbled up through her as she thought of what her parents had told her that morning before school.

Everyone on Emily's table looked surprised. The only person who didn't was Molly, Emily's best friend. Emily had told her the news as soon as she had got in.

"Oh wow! You're going to China?" said Anna across the table.

Miss Haynes clapped her hands for silence. "Everyone, take a break from your maps for a moment. This is very exciting news – Emily's going to China in the holidays. So, are your mum and dad going there because of work, Emily?"

Emily nodded. "They work for WWF . . ."

"WWF is an organization that helps endangered animals and protects the natural world," Miss Haynes explained for anyone who didn't know. "Your mother's a wildlife photographer, isn't she?"

"Yes, and Dad writes articles for the annual newsletter and gets involved with setting up projects," Emily finished. "They've been asked to go to China for a week, although I'm not quite sure why."

"What an adventure!" Miss Haynes went to the computer and, with a bit of quick typing and a few clicks of the mouse, she got the WWF website up on the whiteboard and went to the giant panda section. Immediately a picture came up of a panda climbing a tree. He looked so cuddly there was a chorus of "ahhs".

"He looks just like a teddy bear!" called Anna.

"Pandas *are* part of the bear family, Anna," said Miss Haynes, clicking on another picture of a panda sitting in the snow eating bamboo. "At one time people thought they were more similar to raccoons because of their black and white colouring but research has shown that they are definitely bears. So, what do you know about pandas, Emily?"

Emily grinned. "Lots!"

Miss Haynes, just like everyone in the class, knew that Emily was completely animal mad. She spent all her time reading animal books and magazines, drawing animals and looking at them on the Internet. "Well, they're very rare," Emily started to explain. "Only between one and two thousand are left in the world. They eat bamboo, but with the bamboo forests being cut down they have less food. And they sometimes get caught in traps that poachers set to catch other animals."

The class grew serious. "That's horrible," said Jack.

"Poachers should be stopped," said one of the other boys angrily.

Emily completely agreed. "The WWF are trying to stop them," she explained. "They're creating reserves where the pandas can live. Places where they are safe and there's lots of bamboo – pandas eat for fourteen hours a day!"

"Wish I was a panda!" grinned Jack.

"You'd have to eat bamboo," Molly reminded him.

Jack pulled a face. "Oh yeah."

"That's all very

interesting, Emily," said Miss Haynes. "Now, why don't we have a look at some more pictures?"

A second later, a picture of the most adorable baby panda filled the whiteboard screen.

Everyone squealed.

"Maybe you'll meet a panda cub, Emily," said Molly.

"I'd have to be really lucky for that
– pandas don't have cubs very often so
they're very rare. Not only that, but pandas
are usually really shy." Emily grinned.
"Knowing my luck, I'll probably just see
a whole load of panda poo!"

Anna pulled a face. "OK, maybe you're
not so lucky to be going after all!"

"Pandas poo a lot," Emily told everyone.
"When there are surveys of pandas, the
researchers have to pick up the panda
poo and look inside it."

There was a chorus of disgusted
exclamations.

"Gross!"

"Ew!"

"OK, Emily. I think that's enough
information for now," said Miss Haynes
hastily.

Emily sat down happily. She knew one
thing. She didn't care if she had to wade

through a *lake* of panda poo if it meant she got to see a real panda in the wild! She just couldn't wait for the summer holidays to start!

PANDA PLAYTIME

**For more fun, games
and wild stories, visit
wwf.org.uk/gowild**

WWF